Schott New York

b.1975

STEMS

for piano

Edited by Scott Wollschleger

ED 30100

www.schott-music.com

Mainz · London · Madrid · New York · Paris · Prague · Tokyo · Toronto

Foreword

Alex Mincek's *Stems* starts with a sputter of harmonies in the lower-middle range of the piano. It punctuates an austere, seemingly lifeless soundscape that is colored by the halo of the sostenuto pedal. Slowly climbing up the keyboard, these harmonies erupt in melodic efflorescences or else fight with tenacity, as if against a physical obstacle. The harmonic bursts eventually span almost the entire keyboard, before indulging in riotous, decidedly less secco repetitions. The many fermatas function both to allow a listener to appreciate the kaleidoscopic variety of overtones after the outbursts, and to generate suspense and tension inherent in silence.

Stems is a piece that is at once emphatically abstract and personal, in a sense that the fermatas continuously make the performer shape the musical narrative. One of the more vivid associations that I as performer have with the title is a process of organic growth – the mute drama of plant life blindly, doggedly fighting for survival, expansion and eventual domination.

Yegor Shevtsov
2013

STEMS

Alex Mincek

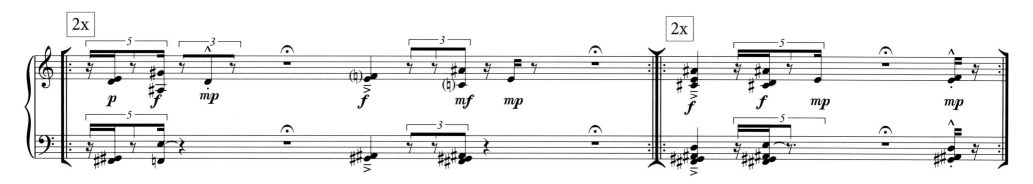

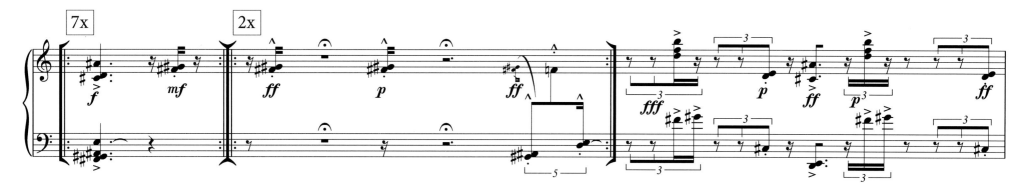

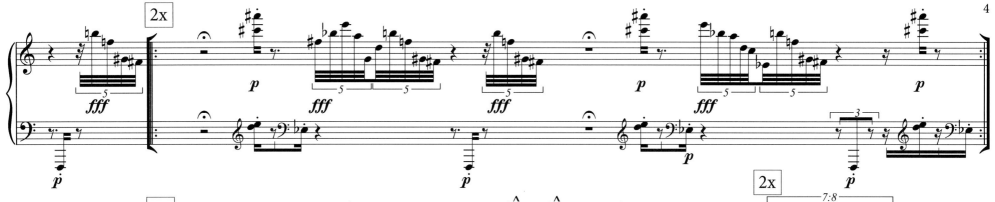

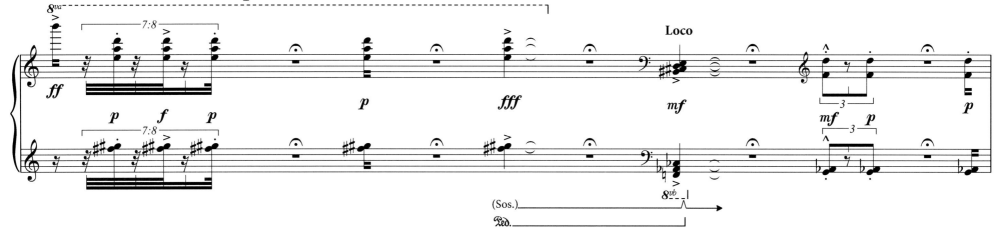

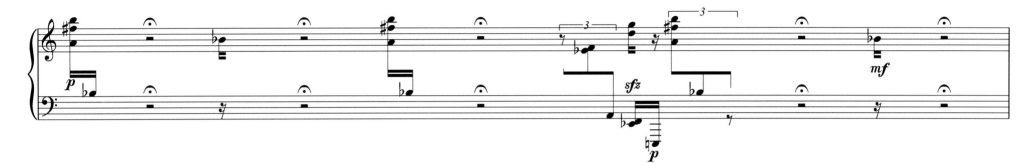

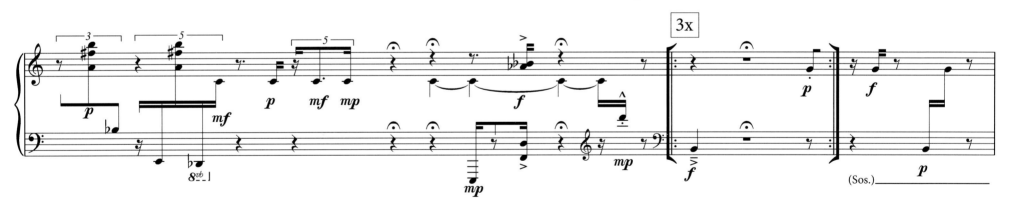

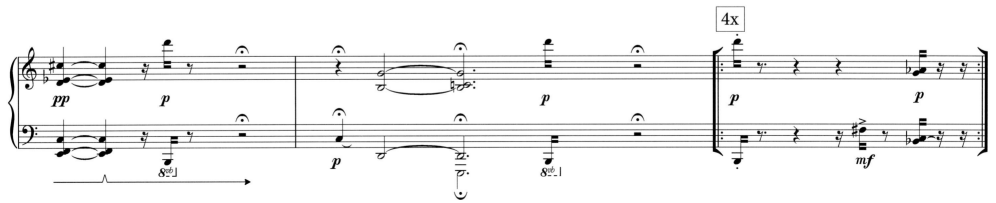

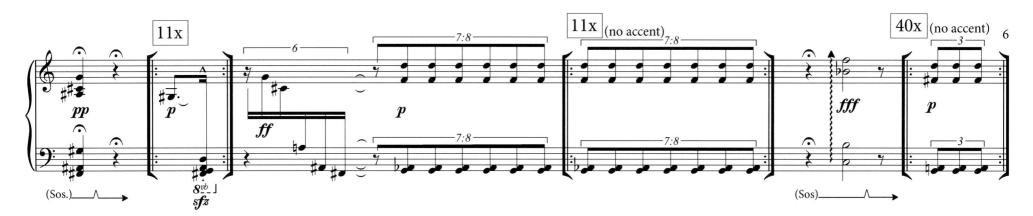

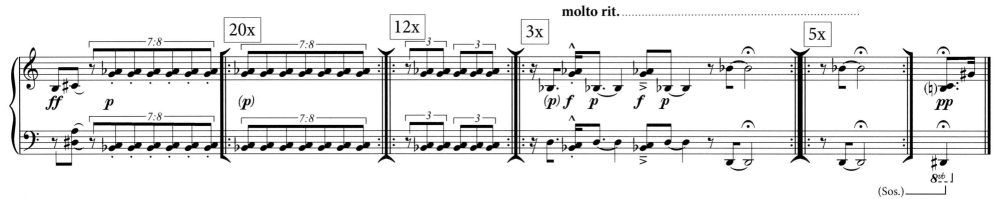

*crescendo through repeat